Language Readers

Level 2
Book E
Units 25–30

Jane Fell Greene
Judy Fell Woods

05   04   7   6

ISBN 1-57035-439-1
ISBN 1-57035-276-3 Set

Text layout and design by Kimberly Harris
Cover design by Becky Malone
Cover Image © 2000 by Digital Vision Ltd.
Illustrated by Peggy Ranson

This product is in compliance with AB2519 California State
Adoption revision requirements.

Printed in the United States of America

Published and Distributed by

SOPRIS
WEST

4093 Specialty Place • Longmont, CO 80504 • (303) 651-2829
www.sopriswest.com

Contents

Unit 25, Book 1

PLEASANT WEATHER

UNIT 25

Phonology/Orthography Concepts

- Two vowel letters that represent one vowel sound (phoneme) create a vowel digraph.
- The vowel digraph **ea** may represent either the short or the long /e/ sound (phoneme).

Vocabulary

bread	head	Ms. Treader	sweat	*their*
breast	headset	pears	sweater	*touch*
breath	health	pleasant	thread	
dead	heaven	read	treadmill	
deaf	heavy	ready	wealth	
dealt	lead	realm	weapon	
death	leapt	spread	weather	
dread	meant	steady		

PLEASANT WEATHER

Story Summary:

PLEASANT WEATHER is a code name Nick, Al, Sam, Sid, and Mat share. It usually means that someone is in trouble and needs help. When Sam receives a coded note in his mailbox, he knows that Al and Nick need him.

Nick and Al would be waiting under the oak tree. Sam took a deep breath. He read their note once more:

Sam: PLEASANT WEATHER.
Bring Mat. Al and Nick.

When Sam spoke to Mat that morning, he told Mat that the note had come. The kids had created the code last summer, so that they could tell each other when one of them needed help. What could it be?

Sam jumped on his bike to meet Mat at the corner. As he pumped his bike up Tenth Street hill, he felt sweat drip from his head. Every thread of his shirt felt wet, but the wind felt chilly as he coasted to the corner. He wished he had worn his sweater like his mom had advised.

PLEASANT WEATHER meant that someone needed help. But who?

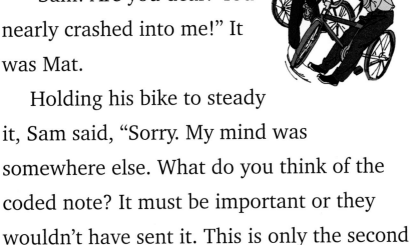

"Sam! Are you deaf? You nearly crashed into me!" It was Mat.

Holding his bike to steady it, Sam said, "Sorry. My mind was somewhere else. What do you think of the coded note? It must be important or they wouldn't have sent it. This is only the second time we have used the code, and I'm scared that there is something big going on."

"Well, let's get to the park," Mat said.

The two of them sailed off to the park on their bikes, both thinking of the many things the note could mean.

Nick and Al were ready and waiting under the oak tree in the park. "What's up?"

asked Mat. "We said we would only use the code in a crisis."

"It's Sid," Nick responded. "We went over to Sid's this morning to help unpack boxes. When we got there, Sid was frantic. Sid was supposed to take care of Hi while his mom was gone. Hi got lost. If his mom gets home before Sid finds Hi, Sid will be punished for a year. He is really sweating it. Sid has got to find Hi," Nick continued. "And we have got to help. We went to find you two, but nobody was home, so we put a note in your mailbox."

"I bet Sid dreads it," Sam said. "His mom is going to kill him. Where does he think Hi is? Did you go over to Carlos's?"

"I did," Nick said. "Bud was over there.

Hi said that he was going over to Carlos's to play, too, but he never got there."

The four of them rode their bikes back to Sid's house. Sid and Hi and their mom had just lived there for two weeks, and they were still unpacking boxes.

From the front porch, Sid yelled, "Has anybody seen Hi yet?" Sid was in a panic. "Mom said I should take care of him. If anything happens to Hi, I have had it. Absolutely. No ifs, ands, or buts!"

On Birch Lane, Hi could never even sit on the steps and play. But when their mom had landed the job, things became much different. Since they had come to their home on Bleaker Street, they could very nearly come and go as they wished.

"Hi said he was ready to go to Carlos's, and he could go by himself," Sid said. "I should have taken him, but I was watching TV, and I wanted to see the end of my program. So I let him go. I dread hearing what Mom will have to say."

Al said, "We need some heavy-duty thinking here. If Hi meant to go to Carlos's house, what way would he have gone?"

Sam interrupted, "What is that? Can you hear that?" At first, they could barely hear it. Could it be a puppy? Maybe. But this cry seemed more like heavy sobbing. They leapt into the street to see what it could be.

The kids ran helter-skelter to the street. At the dead end of the street, standing forlorn, tears streaming, was Hi. Sid held his breath.

"I got lost, Sid. I'm sorry. I tried to find Carlos's, but I kept seeing the same street . . ."

Hi washed up and put on a clean shirt. Just as they got back to the front porch, Sid's and Hi's mom drove up. "Hi, kids. Pleasant weather, huh?" she commented.

"You bet, Mrs. North!" They grinned.

Teacher/Parent Pages

Use the following questions to stimulate language growth, imagination, conceptual relationships, and higher-level thinking skills. These activities will encourage conversation and help develop language skills. Students must know that their ideas are important and that their questions will be heard. Have fun and accept all reasonable answers while praising and encouraging questioning from the students.

Vocabulary Expansion

Describe and define these words and phrases:

helter-skelter	thread of his shirt	sail off
forlorn	emergency	crisis
land a job	reprimand	frantic
deaf	feel sorry for	sweating it
code	steady your bike	heavy-duty thinking

Language Expansion Activities

1. Create a code. Use different words or letters to mean different things. See if your reading group can decode a message written in your code.

2. Write this story from Hi's point of view. Remember to include important key issues. How did he really feel about Sid's not walking him to Carlos's house? It was a new neighborhood, and Hi didn't really know the way. How did Hi feel when he kept passing the same street signs over and over again? How long was he lost?

Language Expansion Questions

1. What did PLEASANT WEATHER mean in this story?

2. What happened to Hi? Why?

3. Why was Sid so upset about Hi's being lost? Have you ever been responsible for a younger child? How do you think your parent(s) would have reacted if you had lost the child?

4. Explain how the boys created their code. Do you think a code is a good way to let someone know you're in trouble? Why do you think codes are used by the military or the FBI?

5. Hi finally found his way home. Have you ever been lost? How did you find your way home? Sometimes it's best to just stay where you are instead of getting more and more confused. What are some other ways of finding your way home?

6. Identify the events in the story that could really happen. Have any of them happened to you?

7. Sid and Hi had just moved into a new neighborhood. Have you ever moved? What are some of the good things about moving? Are there any drawbacks?

8. Imagine that Hi had not shown up. Create a new ending for the story telling how Sid's mom would have reacted. What do you think she would have done first?

9. List three qualities a good brother or sister should possess. Rank them in order of importance. Do you think Sid was a good brother? If you are a brother or sister, rank yourself. Is there any way you could improve?

10. What can we learn about responsibility from this story?

A HEALTH CLUB

UNIT 25

Phonology/Orthography Concepts

- Two vowel letters that represent one vowel sound (phoneme) create a vowel digraph.
- The vowel digraph **ea** may represent either the short or the long /e/ sound (phoneme).

Vocabulary

bread	head	Ms. Treader	sweat	*their*
breast	headset	pears	sweater	*touch*
breath	health	pleasant	thread	
dead	heaven	read	treadmill	
deaf	heavy	ready	wealth	
dealt	lead	realm	weapon	
death	leapt	spread	weather	
dread	meant	steady		

A HEALTH CLUB

Story Summary:

The girls want to become members of the Panthers Junior High Cheerleader Squad. They all passed the first two tryouts easily, but the finals are coming up. They decide that one good way to get in shape is to start a health club.

"Well," said Molly, "we got past the first two cheerleader cuts, but the last one is the hardest." Molly, Pat, Tam, and Kim wanted to be cheerleaders for the Panthers.

Ten girls had passed the first two cuts. Only five would be picked. Ms. Treadwell, the cheerleader coach, would rank the girls.

"Something tells me that I need to get in shape before Wednesday," Tam moaned, gazing at her legs. "I dread performing at school with these flabby legs!"

"May I inquire," grinned Pat, "what it is that you can do between today and Wednesday to repair your legs?"

Kim said, "Tam, your legs are fine."

"We could start a health club in my basement," Molly

said. "Dad gave mom a treadmill for her birthday, but she never uses it."

"My mom sent for one of those sit-up things. She cracks me up," said Kim. "It's still in the box it came in." They snickered.

Molly said, "It's crazy the way they say they are getting in shape and never do it."

"OK," said Kim. "There's the first bell. Why don't we meet at Molly's this afternoon after school?"

"That's a super idea," said Tam, "but I have to baby-sit for the twins after school."

Tam was distressed. She did not think she would make the team. Molly said, "Do not worry, Tam. You can do it. Even if I am not home, you can use the equipment. Deal?"

"Let's go for it," said Tam, Pat, Molly, and Kim. "We could win!"

"I have a math test," said Tam as she locked up her bike and took off her headset. The girls agreed to meet after school.

As she came inside to the den, Molly yelled, "Hi, Mom. I'm home! The girls are coming over to train. We're going to start a health club in the basement. Is that treadmill Dad gave you still there? Can we use it? Do we have any drinks? I need to get some things for us to use."

"Sure, Molly," Mrs. Manchester said. "I would be happy for you to have a health club in the basement."

When Kim and Pat came over, Molly had been doing sit-ups, push-ups, and deep leg bends. She had jogged from one end of the basement to the other fifty times. Sweat was running off her entire body.

"We're ready to start," they said.

"I'm glad you are ready," Molly replied. "I have  had it for today. In fact, I think I have had it forever!" Breathing hard, Molly fell in a heap.

The girls were relentless. Molly, Kim, and Tam trained hard until the following Wednesday. They did the drills each day. When Wednesday came, the girls were scared. Waiting for their turns, Tam said to Pat, "Everybody thinks you will win, but I cannot even do a cartwheel."

But Pat hung her head. She felt bad. She had not done any of the drills that Ms. Treadwell had given them last Tuesday.

"I cannot think what made me try this," Kim muttered. I am so klutzy. I wish I were in bed with the story I read last night."

 Molly's worry was different. She spread her hands. They were shaking. She was new at their school, and lots of kids still had not met her. She suspected that they would make fun of her. "Why did I let myself do this?" she asked herself. A health club was one thing. But getting a spot on the cheerleading team was different.

When it was Tam's turn to perform, Molly touched her hand. "I hope you get it. Just try your best. Do it just like you did yesterday at the health club!"

Pat was next. She was an athlete; she was talented. But she was not ready.

After Kim and Molly had their turns, the girls sat in

the bleachers to wait for the results.

When Ms. Treadwell got up to declare the winners, the girls held hands. "The seventh grade cheerleaders for this year are: Tam Turner, Jane Bleaker, Sis Babcock, Marty Hillstead, and Molly Manchester. Come get your sweaters!"

Pat felt bewildered. Everybody said that she would win, so she had not tried very hard. With Kim it was different. Kim was not athletic and had not expected to win.

Pat kept thinking, "If only I could do it over. I wanted it so badly!" She had to be happy for Molly and Tam, but she felt a big lump in her throat.

Teacher/Parent Pages

Use the following questions to stimulate language growth, imagination, conceptual relationships, and higher-level thinking skills. These activities will encourage conversation and help develop language skills. Students must know that their ideas are important and that their questions will be heard. Have fun and accept all reasonable answers while praising and encouraging questioning from the students.

Vocabulary Expansion

Describe and define these words and phrases:

select	reminisce	letter sweater
shape-up activities	determined	edgy
deal	relentless	tighten up
band together	resolved	cheerleader squad
sit-up rig	declare	exercise equipment

Language Expansion Activities

1. Pretend that you are going to try out for a sports team, marching band, or cheerleader squad. What kinds of exercises and specific training activities would you do? Make a list. Explain why training is important. Try your activities during free time.

2. Draw or cut out pictures of exercise equipment. Make a chart describing each piece of equipment and what specific part of the body it helps to shape up. Make a magazine ad or television commercial for the exercise equipment. Display your ad or videotape your commercial.

Language Expansion Questions

1. What did the girls in this story want to do?

2. What was Molly's idea?

3. Why didn't Tam think that she would make the squad?

4. The girls felt that being in shape was important for the job of cheerleader. Why do you think they felt that way?

5. Cheerleaders have to be in good physical shape. What other jobs require that people be fit and in good physical shape?

6. Describe how Molly felt when Pat and Kim got to her house. How do you feel when you work out for a long time?

7. Molly's mom was supportive of her and her desire to become a cheerleader. How would your parent(s) react if you wanted to start a health club at home?

8. Pat and Kim did not make the squad. What kinds of things could the other girls do to help them feel better? Have you ever missed out on something that you really wanted? How did you feel?

9. The girls wanted to become cheerleaders and they really tried hard. Can you think of something that you want that much? Would you work as hard?

10. When you feel so confident that you don't try, what happens? Can you think of a time that you didn't try your best? Tell the others in the group what happened when you stopped trying.

ALONE AT HOME

UNIT 26

Phonology/Orthography Concepts

- Schwa: In an **unaccented syllable**, the vowel phoneme sound is reduced to the **schwa** /∂/, a reduced short /u/ phoneme.
- Any vowel grapheme may represent the schwa phoneme.

Vocabulary

about	button	Marshall	soda	*build*
across	closet	minute	sofa	*danger*
afraid	department	portable	suddenly	
alone	galloped	problem	supposed	
antenna	kitchen	Ranson		
anthem	local	second		

ALONE AT HOME

Story Summary:

When Nick and Bud come home from school each afternoon, they study, play, and listen to music until their parents come home from work. The boys have a list of "Home Alone Rules." Each afternoon, Nick locks the door, turns on the radio, and phones his mother. One day, a radio announcement frightens Nick.

Nick got the key from under the mat. He never liked to admit it, but he wished that someone were there when he and Bud got home from school.

Their mom let Nick ride his bike, but Bud was just in second grade, and he had to ride the bus home from school. Nick would let him in, and they would turn on some music while they did their homework.

After he hung his coat in the closet, he went in the kitchen and raised the antenna on his dad's portable radio. Suddenly, the music was interrupted:

"Just in from the weather department: Danger. Storm warnings for this area. Tornado headed this way."

His mom had told him to check the bolt, but sometimes he forgot. Nick went to the window to wait for Bud's bus.

It was hard to be home alone. He wished his mom and dad were home. From the window, he saw heavy rain. Trees swayed and branches dropped to the street.

He decided to give his mom a ring and tell her he was home. Nick could never remember his mom's number. He always had to find it on the list she kept in the kitchen. He was pushing the buttons when Bud's bus drove up. He hung up, galloped across the den, and yelled from the window to Bud, "Hurry up, Bud. Get in here!"

Bud ran for the porch, but he fell and dropped his school bag. Papers scattered everywhere. "What's up?" Bud asked.

"Never mind, just get in quick."

Inside, Bud said, "I'm hungry. I want something to eat." The radio interrupted:

"The weather department once more informs us to stay alert, lock up, and remain inside. Tornado headed this way."

"Gee, Nick, what's up? Did you get hold of Mom?" Bud muttered, grabbing a soda and some chips from the pantry.

"The weather report says a tornado is headed this way. We need to stay inside, lock up, and get going on homework," said Nick with a quiver in his throat.

I'm afraid," said Bud from the sofa. "Let's just check the Home Alone List."

Nick was the first to hear the banging on the back porch screen. "Did you hear that?" he asked Bud.

"You get hold of Mom, Bud. I'll check the back porch," Nick said, as he rushed to the kitchen window.

Nick went to check the bolt. The banging kept up. Afraid to open the latch, Nick held his breath until his best buddy, Al, yelled, "Come on, Nick. Let me in. I'm drenched! We were supposed to do our Albert Einstein report after school!"

Relieved, Nick unlocked the screen. "It's just Al," he told Bud.

"Mom was not at her desk," Bud said. "Mrs. Marshall said she would tell her to get hold of us when she gets back."

"Well," Nick said with relief, "Let's finish this snack and start on the report."

"So what's the big problem?" Al asked.

"Did you hear about the tornado warnings?" Nick replied. "I think they said

wind is gusting to 55 MPH
and heavy rain and
thunderstorms are coming
this way."

"Nick, can we just
recheck the Home Alone
List?" Bud asked. The three
read the list taped to the inside of the closet:

Home Alone List
1. Tell Mom when you get home.
2. Never say you are alone.
3. Never let anybody inside.
4. Keep a spare key with Mrs. Ranson.
5. If in danger, use the 911 number.
6. Finish your homework first.
7. Watch TV, play video games, or read.

From the kitchen, the music was
interrupted once more:

*"A report from the local weather
department: The danger is over. The tornado*

warning has ended. Back to the program in progress, Rock Anthems."

"When I grow up, I am going to be a weather reporter and predict when the tornadoes will come," Bud said boldly.

Nick and Al grinned. "I was never afraid," Nick said. "Not for a minute."

"You were, too. You were scared to let Al in. You two are big ninnies. And I'm telling Mom." Bud galloped into the den with Nick and Al in chase.

Teacher/Parent Pages

Use the following questions to stimulate language growth, imagination, conceptual relationships, and higher-level thinking skills. These activities will encourage conversation and help develop language skills. Students must know that their ideas are important and that their questions will be heard. Have fun and accept all reasonable answers while praising and encouraging questioning from the students.

Vocabulary Expansion

Describe and define these words and phrases:

tornado	alarm	get hold of
Albert Einstein	break in on	hold your breath
lonesome	forgetful	interim
storm warnings	stay alert	portable radio
lock up	quiver in his throat	forecast

Language Expansion Activities

1. Go to the library and find a book about tornadoes. Write a report or draw a picture that explains how tornadoes are formed. Share your report with your group, parent(s), or friends.

2. Draw a picture of what Bud looked like when he fell down and dropped all his papers in the pouring rain. Write a paragraph about how he felt. In another paragraph, tell about a time when you have felt that way.

Language Expansion Questions

1. What was the first thing Nick did when he got home from school?

2. Where did Nick find the house key? Where was the spare key?

3. How did Nick feel about being home alone after school? Do you think he felt better when his brother, Bud, got home each day? Would he have felt different if he hadn't had any brothers or sisters?

4. How can a weather forecast help us each day?

5. Nick heard that the tornado winds were gusting to 55 MPH. What does that mean? What kinds of damage can a tornado do?

6. The Home Alone List said that the boys should not let anyone into the house. Why did Nick let Al in? Sometimes we need to make adjustments in the meanings of rules. Think of a rule that your family has had to make adjustments for.

7. Nick couldn't remember his mom's phone number, even though he dialed it every day. Are you good at remembering things like numbers? What are some things we can do to help us remember?

8. Bud was hungry when he got home from school. Do you usually eat a snack when you come home? What is your favorite?

9. Do you sometimes have to go home alone? What is the best thing to do when you do? Have you ever been frightened?

10. Nick and Bud had a Home Alone List. Do you have any lists that your parents have made to help you with your daily activities or with your homework? Share them with your group.

A SEVENTH GRADE PROBLEM

UNIT 26

Phonology/Orthography Concepts

- Schwa: In an **unaccented syllable**, the vowel phoneme sound is reduced to the **schwa** /∂/, a reduced short /u/ phoneme.
- Any vowel grapheme may represent the schwa phoneme.

Vocabulary

about	button	Marshall	soda	*build*
across	closet	minute	sofa	*danger*
afraid	department	portable	suddenly	
alone	galloped	problem	supposed	
antenna	kitchen	Ranson		
anthem	local	second		

A SEVENTH GRADE PROBLEM

Story Summary:

Nick has always had problems in reading, writing, and spelling. His teacher wants to help him, but Nick is embarrassed. Ms. Silver asks another teacher, who happens to be Nick's neighbor, to talk to Nick and his parents about helping him. Nick can't believe it when Mr. Ranson tells him that he is really very smart.

"I'm getting sick of trying," said Nick to himself. He had studied hard for that science test. But he had failed once more.

As the students left her class, Ms. Silver stopped Nick. "Could you come by for a minute after school?" she asked.

"I don't think so. My mom says . . ."

"Nick, I can see that you have worked hard . . ."

Nick felt his head spin. What would

happen to him? They had held him back in second grade, and now he could fail once more. What was the matter? Why was it so hard for him to read and spell when it seemed so easy for everybody else?

Even Al didn't realize how much Nick dreaded reading in class. Each time a teacher said his name, he wished he could disappear.

What Nick wanted to do was to get out of school and repair cars and build motors. That was what his dad did, and even his dad said Nick had a real talent with motors.

Ms. Silver was sitting at her desk waiting for Nick. He was ready for the punishment. "I know how bad I have been doing in science, Ms. Silver," he began.

"I am not angry, Nick. I've seen how hard you have worked," Ms. Silver told him, "particularly since Al started helping you after school. But there is something else that could help."

"Thanks, Ms. Silver, but nobody can help me. I'm just not smart.

"Mom has tried lots of times to help me with spelling," Nick said. "But after I think I have the words, I still get mixed up." Nick could not keep back his tears.

Ms. Silver put her arm around Nick and handed him a napkin. "Have you ever met Mr. Ranson?"

Nick said, "Mr. Ranson and his wife live next to us, Ms. Silver. He plays tennis with my dad. Mrs. Ranson is an artist. She works at home. She keeps the key for us."

Just then, Mr. Ranson appeared. "Hi, Nick. Hello, Ms. Silver."

"Hi," Nick responded. He could not understand why Mr. Ranson was there.

Maybe Mr. Ranson was going to tell his mom and

dad how bad he had been doing. Why else would he be there? Nick had never felt so depressed in his life.

"Did you hear me, Nick? I said that Mr. Ranson had something to tell you." Nick raised his head and put on a smile. He liked Mr. Ranson.

Mr. Ranson began, "Nick, I have seen how much talent you have. Sometimes, I cannot believe the things that you do with motors and the complex models you build. And the way you play the sax! You do not even read music, but you are better than I am!" Mr. Ranson was trying to console him, but Nick felt plain failure.

"That's what Mr. Ranson told me, too, Nick," remarked Ms. Silver. "So we wanted to have Mr. Ranson give you some tests to see what we can do to help you."

"Yes," Mr. Ranson declared. "I will speak to your mom and dad when I get home. I think we can help you, Nick."

On the way home, Nick considered what they had said to him. Would he have to be separated from Al and the rest of his pals? Nick did not want to think what could happen, but he could not stop worrying. Even Bud did better in school than Nick.

Maybe his mom and dad would get home too late to talk to Mr. Ranson. Nick realized that Mr. Ranson worked at school, but he never asked what he did there. He was sort of a teacher, but lots of kids from different classes went to him at different times. "Forget it," he muttered to himself. He would go home and finish building his model of the Desert Storm tank.

After dinner, when Nick and Bud were doing the dishes, Mr. Ranson came over. He went into the den with their mom and dad. They were in there a long time.

Later, Nick's mom and dad said, "At last somebody understands your problem. Mr. Ranson said some kids are smart, but they need different kinds of teaching. He said some teachers are trained to help smart kids who have problems in reading and spelling. You are smart, Nick. At last, we think Mr. Ranson has the answer for us."

Nick was stunned. Could he really be smart? No teacher had said that before.

Teacher/Parent Pages

Use the following questions to stimulate language growth, imagination, conceptual relationships, and higher-level thinking skills. These activities will encourage conversation and help develop language skills. Students must know that their ideas are important and that their questions will be heard. Have fun and accept all reasonable answers while praising and encouraging questioning from the students.

Vocabulary Expansion

Describe and define these words and phrases:

sick of trying	depressed	auto mechanic
failure	learning disabilities	read music
felt his head spin	special education	console
defeated	keep back the tears	conference
self-esteem	complex models	stunned

Language Expansion Activities

1. Act out this story with your group. Choose people to play the roles of Nick, Ms. Silver, Mr. Ranson, and Nick's parents. Write the dialogue for the conversation Mr. Ranson has with Mr. and Mrs. Hopkins.

2. Why are tanks built on tracks instead of wheels? When are tanks better than jeeps or other vehicles? Make a chart that shows the advantages of tanks. Try to find a book in the library to help you with your chart.

Language Expansion Activities

1. What course was Nick failing?

2. Why was Nick tired of trying to do better in school? Have you ever felt that way about anything? Did anyone ever try to help?

3. Why did Ms. Silver want Nick to stop by her room after school? Who was there with her?

4. Mr. Ranson was a special education teacher. What kinds of things does he do in school? Do you know any teachers like him?

5. Nick had to stay back in second grade. What does that mean?

6. Nick has a lot of trouble learning, but there are many things he does well. Can you name the things Nick does well? What are some of the things you do well? Are there any subjects that you need help with?

7. Nick said that each time a teacher said his name he wanted to disappear. Have you ever felt that way? If you could disappear just once each day, when would it be? Why?

8. Nick wanted to repair cars and build motors. Is it important for him to learn how to read and write if that is the job he wants? Why is it important for everybody to learn to read and write no matter what job they have in life?

9. Discuss what Ms. Silver did for Nick. Has a teacher ever helped you that way? Share your story with your group.

10. Predict what will happen when Mr. Ranson tests Nick. Will Nick be able to get some special help from Mr. Ranson? What kinds of things might Mr. Ranson do to help Nick?

THE NOTE IN THE BOTTLE

UNIT 27

Morphology/Orthography Concepts

- The sixth syllable type is a consonant letter **(-c) + -le**.
  - **c + le** exists only at the end of a word, and only in words of more than one syllable.
  - **c + le** represents the sounds of -consonant + schwa + l.

Vocabulary

baffle	jiggle	responsible	tangle	*gone*
boggle	juggle	riddle	tremble	*none*
bottle	kettle	ruffle	tumble	*one*
bundle	ladle	sample	wiggle	*son*
crackle	little	simple	wobble	*though*
dawdle	marble	sizzle		*thought*
Eagle	mumble	steeple		*won*
hassle	nestle	stumble		
hobble	people	table		
idle	puzzle	tackle		

THE NOTE IN THE BOTTLE

Story Summary:

Sam stumbles upon a bottle while he is walking to the pet shop. The bottle has a note in it. He takes it out to read it, but can't understand the riddle written on the paper. He decides to take the note to Ted Conrad at the shell shop, hoping that Ted can help decipher the riddle.

"What a hassle," Sam remarked as he juggled cans and bottles from the parking lot into the little convenience store.

Each Saturday morning, Sam returned bottles and cans to the store. He usually carried them in his bike basket, but today there had been too many, so his dad drove. "Ready to go, son?" Mr. Webster asked.

"I don't mind going home by myself, Dad. I wanted to stop by Jen Wells' Pet Shop and see the little lab pups anyway."

"I have no problem with that, son. See you back at the ranch," Mr. Webster said as he drove away.

Sam stumbled off toward the dock and Jen Wells' Pet Shop. He was sitting watching for the ships in the harbor when something reflected at the water's edge.

Sam bent over. A marble-like bottle was nestled in the mud. Sam dug into the dirt, freed it, and washed it off in the water. He saw something inside. Was it paper?

"What the . . ." he mumbled to himself as he tried to get the cap off the bottle. He wiggled and twisted the bottle cap, but it didn't move. Not even an inch. Finally, he put some real power in his twist, and the cap fell onto the grass.

"A note!" exclaimed Sam. He read:

"Jiggle tremble tumble wiggle
'til you find a bundle simple
in a church that has a steeple
on a street with many people."

"This seems like a puzzle for Ted Conrad." Sam mumbled the words to the riddle once more. Ted's Shell Shop was only a few steps

 away. Gazing in that direction, Sam spotted Ted eating an apple.

"Ted! Ted!" yelled Sam. "I think I have the story of the year! Wait 'til you see what was in this bottle I got from the mud!"

"Slowly, Sam. Show me what you have there. I'm somewhat baffled by your bottle. What exactly have you got there?"

"It's a marble bottle, Ted," explained Sam. "I found it on the way to the dock. Will you help me tackle the riddle inside?"

"Riddle?" inquired Ted.

After Ted read the note, he said, "This is a real puzzle, my son. A real puzzle. The bottle itself is a rare one. 1700s, I think. And it could have come from as

far away as Japan.
Never seen such a
rare sample." Sam
was getting more and
more interested. Secret puzzles like this one
enchanted Ted as much as they did Sam.

"I can only think of two churches with
steeples here in this port," Ted said.

"Would those be the Tenth Street
Cathedral and the church over on Bleaker,
Ted?" asked Sam. "Both of those streets have
many people."

"Just so, lad," Ted replied. "Just so. Let's
take a little trek over to Tenth Street. And
bring that note with you." Flipping his sign
from OPEN to CLOSED, Ted
hobbled off. Secretly, Ted was
as excited as Sam.

Once inside the cathedral,
they found a priest. But he
could remember no bundle

being found. "The cathedral was totally restored over the past ten years," he added.

There was just one more place to investigate. The two detectives hiked to the Bleaker Street church. But even if this was the church, would they find a bundle?

The minister was speaking to a lady when Ted and Sam got there. Sam showed them the note and the bottle. "Have you heard about a secret bundle inside your church?" Sam asked.

"I have played the organ here for more than thirty years," interrupted the lady. "And for thirty years, I've prayed that one day someone would find that note!"

"What?" The minister was puzzled. "No one told me anything about a note!"

"It was a secret," confided the organist. "Long ago, two sailors made a pact. They put

a note in that bottle and said that on the day
the bottle was found, we could sell the
bundle's contents and distribute the profits
to the needy. They said that by the time the
bottle was found, the bundle would be worth
a fortune."

"And you know where it is hidden?"

"In the boards behind my organ," she
said, "waiting for the bottle to wash up."

"Credit must be given to this lad," Ted
said. "Because of him, this church will be
able to help many people!"

Sam had never felt so happy!

Teacher/Parent Pages

Use the following questions to stimulate language growth, imagination, conceptual relationships, and higher-level thinking skills. These activities will encourage conversation and help develop language skills. Students must know that their ideas are important and that their questions will be heard. Have fun and accept all reasonable answers while praising and encouraging questioning from the students.

Vocabulary Expansion

Describe and define these words and phrases:

convenience store	dumbfounded	Japan
recycle	tackle a riddle	enchanted
Labrador pups	story of the year	cathedral
what a hassle	1700s	worth a fortune
see you back at the ranch	rare bottle	wash up

Language Expansion Activities

1. Act out the story, letting each student pretend to find the bottle. Each time you act out the story, write a different riddle to put inside the bottle. If you can't think of your own riddle, go to the library and take out a book of riddles. See if you can fool anyone with your riddle.

2. Draw the ship in which the two sailors put out to sea after they hid the bottle. Write a description of the ship and share it with the group.

Language Expansion Questions

1. What were Sam and his father doing at the local convenience store? Do you ever recycle cans with your parents? Why is it important?

2. Sam did not go home with his dad. Where did he say he was going? Did he ever get there? Where did he go instead? Why?

3. Along the way to the pet shop, Sam sat down at the edge of the water to rest. Describe the way it feels to sit and rest at the edge of water. Why do people enjoy going near water for vacations?

4. Some people are just plain lucky. Why was Sam lucky in this story? Have you ever been lucky? Share your experience.

5. Try to memorize the riddle in the bottle. Let everyone have a turn at reciting it. Think of something that you have memorized and share it with your group.

6. The note in the bottle was a riddle. Ted said that it was a puzzle. How can a riddle be a puzzle? Can you think of a riddle?

7. Some people would say that Ted and Sam went on a "wild goose chase." Can you explain what that means? Is it true?

8. The organist at the church kept a secret for 30 years. Have you ever kept a secret? Why are there some people who can keep a secret better than others? What makes someone trustworthy?

9. What do you think was in the bundle hidden behind the organ boards? How will it help many people? What makes a person "needy?"

10. Pretend that you are Sam Webster. What will you tell your parents when you go home? What will you tell your friends?

A FINE KETTLE OF FISH

UNIT 27

Morphology/Orthography Concepts

- The sixth syllable type is a consonant letter **(-c) + -le**.
  - **c + le** exists only at the end of a word, and only in words of more than one syllable.
  - **c + le** represents the sounds of -consonant + schwa + l.

Vocabulary

baffle	jiggle	responsible	tangle	*gone*
boggle	juggle	riddle	tremble	*none*
bottle	kettle	ruffle	tumble	*one*
bundle	ladle	sample	wiggle	*son*
crackle	little	simple	wobble	*though*
dawdle	marble	sizzle		*thought*
Eagle	mumble	steeple		*won*
hassle	nestle	stumble		
hobble	people	table		
idle	puzzle	tackle		

A FINE KETTLE
OF FISH

Story Summary:

Sam Webster had found a note in a bottle near the
dock. The note led to a treasure which would be used
to help the needy people of the town. Sam's friend, Ted
Conrad at Ted's Shell Shop, has a party to thank Sam
for helping so many others. The party is a success in
spite of the antics of some playful pups.

Local Lad Finds Fantastic Bundle, the headline read. Sam's story had made the front page of the Sunday morning paper.

As the Websters were finishing their waffles, Sam's dad said, "Well, son, did you ever think that the note you found in the marble bottle would come to this?"

Sam had become a local hero when he had discovered a marble bottle near the docks. The note inside it was put there years before by two sailors. The note referred to a bundle hidden in a church. Sam had been responsible for finding the bundle. When its contents were cashed in, the profits would go to the needy.

"It boggles my mind, Dad." Sam was still overwhelmed. "It still seems like a story from TV or something.

"One thing still puzzles me, though. Why do you think the organist never said anything about the bundle she kept behind that organ? What kind of mumbo jumbo had those sailors done on her? None of it makes sense. You would have thought she would have said something . . . ."

But before Sam could finish, there was banging on their back porch screen. "Sam! Sam! Where's the local hero?"

Mat, Sid, Al, and Nick, Sam's best pals, were waiting to hear the real story.

"Do you still have the marble bottle?" Al wondered.

"Can I touch you, man?" said Nick.

"I was just about to go over to Ted's Shell Shop," Sam said. "He asked my dad if I could go over there this morning and give them a hand with something. If you go with me, we could do the job faster."

Sam grabbed his jacket and added, "Mom, we are going to Ted's. Be back for lunch."

Sam's mom gave his dad a secret smile. They had spoken to Ted early that morning,  and were aware of the big surprise that Ted had in store for their son. Mr. and Mrs. Webster were on their way to the docks, too, along with lots of other people from their village.

Sam was astonished at what was waiting at the docks. Banners and flags ruffled in the wind. A fire crackled under the big kettle Ted used for huge gatherings.

There were clams, shrimp, lobsters, and crabs. Sam thought the entire village must be there. One huge banner read, "Sam Webster—Local Hero."

Everyone was ready to help. Ted was in charge, with Mat's parents, Chick and Pam Miller, helping him. The shop owners at the dock had pitched in to prepare this feast for Sam.

Last summer, Sam had worked for Jen Wells, who owned the pet shop. Jen had a wonderful gift for Sam. As she got out of her van, Jen's gift escaped with her. One of the lab pups that Sam had come to visit was wearing a red banner: "Sam, I am yours."

It was Eagle, Sam's favorite little lab. Sam was excited. He thought of his fat cat, Max, though. He wondered if Eagle and Max could ever become pals.

"Don't dawdle, son," Ted said gruffly. "I need some help if we are going to be able to feed an entire village. Bring those other idle lads over here and lend me a hand!"

The band began to play. Everyone began to sing and dance. The fire under Ted's kettle sizzled. But just as Ted was adding the shrimp to the kettle, Eagle got into a tangle with some stray cats. As they began their chase, Ted's big table began to wobble and everything went topsy-turvy.

Ted chased the cats with his ladle. Sam finally grabbed Eagle and got her back into Jen's van. But the meal was gone. The entire table had spilled onto the dock.

That night, as Mr. and Mrs. Webster and the shop

owners left the dock with Sam and his pals, they spoke of the village people and how they had saved the party.

Just when they had thought there was no hope, everyone had done something to help. Some had helped Ted clean the mess. The cats had helped, too. And many people had gone home to bring things back to the dock. In the end, they had had plenty. They could have fed an army.

"Ted, I think we had a Fine Kettle of Fish anyway!" Sam said.

"Me, too," added Mat with a burp.

Teacher/Parent Pages

Use the following questions to stimulate language growth, imagination, conceptual relationships, and higher-level thinking skills. These activities will encourage conversation and help develop language skills. Students must know that their ideas are important and that their questions will be heard. Have fun and accept all reasonable answers while praising and encouraging questioning from the students.

Vocabulary Expansion

Describe and define these words and phrases:

a fine kettle of fish	contents	to have in store
newspaper headline	the needy	banner
front page	overwhelmed	pitch in
local hero	profit	topsy-turvy
cash in	mumbo jumbo	get into a tangle

Language Expansion Activities

1. Write a newspaper story about Sam's adventure. Have each person in the group write a different headline for your story. Vote for the best one. Submit your story to your school paper.

2. Visit a local newspaper or printing company. When you return, prepare a report about how newspapers are written, or how printers work. Give your report orally to the group.

Language Expansion Questions

1. What did the headline in the Sunday morning paper say?

2. Tell what facts the newspaper story should have included.

3. The story states: "Sam's mom gave his dad a secret smile." Why was it a secret smile? What did it mean?

4. Sam thought he was going over to Ted's to help with some chores. Why was he really going to Ted's? Have you ever been surprised? Tell what happened to you.

5. Nick said, "Can I touch you, man?" What did he really mean?

6. The story never told us what was in that bundle behind the organ. What could it have been? Do you think the authors should have told us? Why do writers sometimes leave something for the reader to try to figure out? Why is that sometimes a fun thing to do when you are reading?

7. The story says that the shop owners all pitched in to prepare the feast for Sam. What does that mean? Has your family ever pitched in with others to prepare a feast? Describe the event.

8. Sam was excited when Jen Wells gave him a new pet. But he was not sure if his cat, Max, would get along with the dog. What are some characteristics of a good pet? List them.

9. What would you have done if you had been Ted and the animals had destroyed your dinner?

10. Do you think the village people made the right decision in the end when everyone brought food from their homes? Why did Sam say that the meal was a "Fine Kettle of Fish" anyway?

THE LONG RIDGE ROAD FESTIVAL

UNIT 28

Phonology/Orthography Concepts

- The phonogram **-dge** comes at the end of a one-syllable word, after a short vowel.
  - **-dge** represents the /j/ phoneme.

Vocabulary

bridge	fidgety	judge	pledge	*another*
budge	fudge	judgment	ridge	*brother*
budget	gadget	lodge	smudge	*eye*
Dodger	hedge	lodger	trudge	*mother*
edge	hedged	midget	wedge	*other*
fidget	hedgehog	nudge		

THE LONG RIDGE ROAD FESTIVAL

Story Summary:

The Long Ridge Road Festival is an annual harvest celebration that features homemade foods and crafts as well as entertainment by local people. During this year's festival, Pat and Kim are inspired by the singing of the Long Ridge Glee Club, a community chorus from their hometown. They discover that one of their heroes is a member of the club.

Pat and Kim were excited. The Long Ridge Road Festival would be held today and they were at Kim's getting ready to go.

The festival, an important event in Jasper, was held each year near a lodge that dated back to 1726. To get there, you had to pass under a covered bridge. The leaves were turning, and it was a perfect day. Handmade quilts, pumpkin pies, fudge, and other items would be judged at the festival. Square dancers, storytellers, and the Long Ridge Glee Club

 would provide some of the entertainment.

"Mother, where is my silver hair clip?" asked Kim, pulling back strands of her hair.

"Wherever you put it," said Mrs. Chung. "Just use your other one. But hurry! I have to get my pie there on time."

Mrs. Chung eyed her freshly baked pumpkin pie. She thought it was the best one she had ever made. "I have a feeling that the judges could rank my pumpkin pie the 'Best in Show,'" she said to herself.

The wheels of Mrs. Chung's car hobbled across the covered bridge until at last, the girls could see the festival tents. "Wow!" exclaimed Pat. "It's even better than last year!" Pat's mother had died when she was just six. Since then, Kim's mom had been like a second mother to Pat. She spent a lot of time at the Chungs'.

Aromas from kitchen tents made them hungry, so they decided to eat lunch first.

The two girls saw Dan Burger carrying his red and purple glee club robe into the music tent. "Did you hear what Mother said?" asked Kim. "Dan is going to play soccer for Rutgers. My mother was Dan's teacher when he was in the ninth grade."

"Once Dan came to demonstrate for my soccer team," Pat remarked. "But he would never remember me."

"I never would have thought he could sing, too!" Kim commented. "It is hard to get into the Long Ridge Glee Club. They are one of the best there is. They win as many contests as the soccer team. Let's go inside and listen to them."

The tent was filled with people. Everyone rose when the band began to play "The Star-Spangled Banner." Kim and Pat sang

 along. It was such a wonderful song that as they sang, tears came to their eyes. Even the little ones did not fidget during the anthem. After the song, the people pledged to the flag in unison.

Tam touched Pat on the back. "Did you save us a seat?" she asked. "This is Molly's first festival, and she adores it!"

"Just squeeze in between us," Pat said. "We want to hear the glee club sing. They were invited to sing for the President at the Cherry Blossom Festival next spring!"

"No kidding? Lucky ducks! I wish I could be in the glee club," said Tam.

Kim nudged Tam. "Shhh. It's starting." A hush fell over the tent. Standing on the risers, the Long Ridge Glee Club lifted their heads, eyes on their director, and began: *I hear a song coming on. It's a melody . . . .*

The people stayed on the edges of their seats. As the glee club left the tent, Mrs. Chung edged in beside Kim. "I am tickled pink," she said. "What do you think? After trying for five years, I have won the 'Best in Show' ribbon for my pumpkin pie!"

"Mother! Really?" Kim glowed with pride. "That's wonderful!"

Pat said, "OK, Mrs. Chung. So can we have a wedge of that pie? You said we had to wait 'til after the contest. So can we?"

"Sorry, Pat. The judges said the winners had to leave everything for the display! But when we get back home, I will make a pie just for you!"

By seven o'clock, the contests had ended, the

people were fed, the pies were judged, and the songs were sung. Another Long Ridge Road Festival had ended.

Passing under the covered bridge and heading for home, Kim said, "I wish we could be in the glee club, Pat. I have taken lessons since I was seven. And you are a wonderful singer. Mom said so."

Mrs. Chung said, "You both wanted to be cheerleaders, and were unhappy to be cut. But remember, it took me five years to get a ribbon for my pie. Just keep trying." Pat and Kim eyed each other. Would they try once more?

Teacher/Parent Pages

Use the following questions to stimulate language growth, imagination, conceptual relationships, and higher-level thinking skills. These activities will encourage conversation and help develop language skills. Students must know that their ideas are important and that their questions will be heard. Have fun and accept all reasonable answers while praising and encouraging questioning from the students.

Vocabulary Expansion

Describe and define these words and phrases:

festival	handmade quilt	displays
tickled pink	annual event	glee club robe
bobbing for apples	sundry items	fifth in state
glee club	Best in Show	sing in unison
square dancers	aroma	anthem

Language Expansion Activities

1. Pretend that you and your group are planning a festival like the Long Ridge Road Festival. Make a list of all the things you would like to have at the festival. Give each person a job to do such as director of the choir, pie judge, quilt judge, food tent supervisor, etc. Explain why planning an event such as an annual festival takes so much time.

2. Mrs. Chung had to cross a covered bridge in order to get to the festival. Go to the library and find a book about covered bridges. Find out as much as you can about that kind of bridge and write some facts about it. Share your research with your group.

Language Expansion Questions

1. What was the name of the festival? Why do you think it was given that name?

2. What was Kim's mom doing for the festival? Why was it so important for her to be on time?

3. List the different tents mentioned at the festival. Do you think there were others as well? What might they have been?

4. Explain why the girls were so enamored of Dan Burger. Do you have any heroes? Who are they? Why are they your heroes?

5. Kim's mom's pie won "Best in Show." What three criteria would you use if you were the pie-tasting judge? Why?

6. Compare Kim and Pat's longing to be in the glee club to their desire to become cheerleaders. Why is it important to keep trying out for things even if you don't make it the first time?

7. Predict what it will be like for the two girls if they decide to try out for the Long Ridge Glee Club. What will happen?

8. Imagine that you are at the festival. What events would you like the best? What tent would you go into first; last; never?

9. Suppose that Kim's mom hadn't won a blue ribbon for her pie. How might she have felt? Do you think she would bake another pie next year? How do you know? What would you do?

10. Judge whether or not the festival was a success. How did you reach your conclusion? Have you ever been to a festival? Did you have a good time? Does that make it a success?

THE GLEE CLUB

UNIT 28

Phonology/Orthography Concepts

- The phonogram **-dge** comes at the end of a one-syllable word, after a short vowel.
  - **-dge** represents the /j/ phoneme.

Vocabulary

bridge	fidgety	judge	pledge	*another*
budge	fudge	judgment	ridge	*brother*
budget	gadget	lodge	smudge	*eye*
Dodger	hedge	lodger	trudge	*mother*
edge	hedged	midget	wedge	*other*
fidget	hedgehog	nudge		

THE GLEE CLUB

Story Summary:

Each year, the Long Ridge Glee Club holds auditions for new members. There are singers of all ages in this famous community chorus. The group has been chosen to sing for the President next spring, and many people are eager to become members. Pat and Kim decide to try out.

 "Who but you could be late on a day like today?" Pat chided Kim. "I nearly left without you."

"I hear you. I had to find something to wear. Are we ready to go?"

"Your mother was going to drive us," Pat said, "but she left. I hope you are happy that I waited for you."

Kim was on edge. Kim thought she wanted to try for a spot in the Long Ridge Glee Club. But the day had come, and inside, she was trembling.

"What can happen?" Pat said. "Even if we are not picked, we can try next year. They probably never take anybody before ninth grade, anyway."

Pals since kindergarten, Pat and Kim shared the bond of having only one parent. Kim thought Pat's dad was the smartest man

she ever met. Kim's father
and mother were separated.
She never got to see her dad.

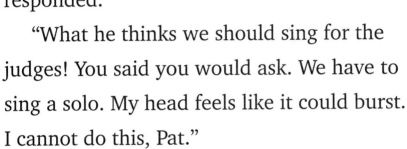

"Did you ask your dad?"
Kim asked.

"Ask him what?" Pat
responded.

"What he thinks we should sing for the
judges! You said you would ask. We have to
sing a solo. My head feels like it could burst.
I cannot do this, Pat."

"Yes, you can. Remember what your mom
said: 'People who never try never win.'
Unlock your bike. Let's get going."

The two girls raced to
the corner, just as they had
done since kindergarten.

They spotted Pat's dad
driving to work. "Break a
leg!" he yelled. When they
did something important,

he always said that. He said it would bring them luck.

Pat's little sister, Trish, was in the car with him. Trish yelled out to them, "Break both of your legs!" Pat and Kim got tickled and had to stop. Trish was a funny kid.

Before they got past Mr. Martin's

supermarket, they could see the cars waiting to get across Long Ridge Bridge. Could everyone be coming to sing for the music director? Kim wished her mom were here. A little shy, Kim felt fidgety and tense.

They parked their bikes behind the lodge. "Get the music," Pat reminded Kim. They headed into the lodge with what seemed like a hundred other people. Just six would be selected.

In big red letters, cards directed them to the lines where they had  to wait their turns. Pat located the alto line. "Where do the sopranos go?" A gray-haired lady in front of Kim said, "Follow me. I am a soprano, too. This will be the tenth year I have tried for a spot in this glee club. But I would keep trying just to hear their music."

As people were called to the stage to perform, Pat felt uneasy. Her turn was next. She did not think she was the singer Kim was. And lots of the other people were vying for spots in the glee club.

"Is this your first time?" asked a short, heavy red-headed lady in back of Pat.

"Yes ma'am, it is," said Pat, clearing her throat. Pat thought about the day she had tried for the cheerleader squad and was cut. Everyone had said she would win, but she had not. The lady was still chattering.

"I have stood in this line before. Since they chose the glee club to sing for the President, everyone wants in!"

Pat wondered whether Kim had sung yet. Pat's dad called Kim "the little diva." In opera, that meant a great soprano. But nobody ever said Pat was a diva.

The director had asked Kim to sing two times. Then he had asked her to wait.

Over the intercom, Pat heard her name. Stepping up to the stage, she felt her legs wobble. Her throat closed.

Kim sat and waited. Why had he asked her to sing once more? The others were such fine singers! Kim thought there was no hope. She had begun to search for Pat. Then, the director said that he had chosen two sopranos. Kim held her breath.

When the director said "Kim Chung," she had to stop and wonder who that was!

But how could she tell Pat? First, Pat had wanted to be a cheerleader and was not chosen. This time, Kim was chosen for the glee club. The little lump in Kim's throat would not go away.

Suddenly, from stage left, Kim heard a screeching roar. It could only be a tiger or Pat. "I made it! Kim! Get up here on this stage!" The two hugged each other, and together, they stepped on the risers to sing.

Pat felt a nudge on her back. It was Dan Burger, the star of the Jasper Cats soccer team. "Glad you made it, Pat," he said.

Teacher/Parent Pages

Use the following questions to stimulate language growth, imagination, conceptual relationships, and higher-level thinking skills. These activities will encourage conversation and help develop language skills. Students must know that their ideas are important and that their questions will be heard. Have fun and accept all reasonable answers while praising and encouraging questioning from the students.

Vocabulary Expansion

Describe and define these words and phrases:

screeching roar

little lump in your throat

chide

on edge

tryouts

share a bond

repertoire

sing a solo

alto

soprano

break a leg

vying for a spot

diva

throat closed

nudge each other

Language Expansion Activities

1. Pretend that you are going to have glee club tryouts. What songs would your group sing for the judges? Make a list of the songs you and your group would like to sing. Select group members to be the judges and the singers. Conduct a tryout session. Perhaps your teacher could tape-record your session.

2. Write a description of the Long Ridge Road Lodge and gardens. How old is it? What does it look like? How much land is it on? What kind of architecture is it? After you finish writing your description, draw a picture to illustrate it.

Language Expansion Questions

1. Where were Kim and Pat going? Why?

2. Did Kim and Pat have the same kind of voices? Look back in the text and find out what their voice types were called. What type voice do you have? How could you find out?

3. In the beginning of the story, it states that Kim was "on edge." She snapped at Pat and was slow getting ready. Have you ever been "on edge?"

4. What thoughts do you suppose Pat and Kim had right before they had to try out for the judges? Have you ever felt like that?

5. Pat and Kim shared the bond of having only one parent. Pat's mom died when she was young, and Kim's parents were separated. Why is it hard to have only one parent to share your life with? How can being an orphan be even more difficult?

6. Suppose Pat had not been selected for the glee club? How would the story have been different? Create a new ending.

7. How would you describe the feelings of the people who came to the tryouts that day?

8. Suppose that the girls were trying out for a spot on the baseball team. Would the story be different? Do most people have the same feelings no matter what sport or team or club they are vying for? Have you ever tried out for anything? Share it.

9. Decide which character in the story you would like to be. Think of three reasons why you would want to be that character.

10. Judge whether this was a good story. List your reasons.

THE ZOO TRIP

UNIT 29

Phonology/Orthography Concepts

- A **vowel digraph** is composed of two vowel letters (graphemes) that represent one vowel sound (phoneme).
- The vowel digraph **oo** represents two different phonemes.

Vocabulary

baboon	good	noon	smooth	*father*
balloon	goody	overtook	stood	*honest*
boost	lagoon	pontoon	stoop	*honor*
boot	look	roof	tooth	*hour*
booth	loose	scoop	zoo	*watch*
broom	moose	shampoo		

THE ZOO TRIP

Story Summary:

Kim's mother, Mrs. Chung, and Al's father, Mr. Long, take Kim, Al, Bud, and Nick to the zoo for the day. Kim takes too long to get ready, Bud has a loose tooth, and there is a problem on the way to the zoo gate. But once inside, they have a wonderful time. Mrs. Chung discusses her ninth grade class with Mr. Long.

"Hurry up, Kim," said Mrs. Chung as she smoothed the cloth on the kitchen table. "The Longs will be here soon and we said we would be ready for the zoo trip by noon."

"Mother," Kim yelled. "My hair looks like a wet broom. I finished shampooing it, but I have to dry it. I cannot greet Al and his father looking like this," she added. "They will think they have already gotten to the zoo!"

"OK, dear," replied Mrs. Chung, "but if you do not hurry up, I will have to come up there! We will be an hour late!"

The bell rang. Al, Mr. Long, Bud, and Nick stood on the stoop. "Please come in," said Mrs. Chung with a smile.

"I hope you don't mind that Nick and Bud came with us," said Al. "This will be Bud's first trip to the zoo."

"Good! This will be a wonderful day, if Kim ever gets ready," said Mrs. Chung. "Kim could win honors for being late!"

Bud said, "My tooth is loose, Mrs. Chung! Honest! Mr. Long, look!"

Al and Nick sat on the stoop to wait. "Girls!" Nick said. "They always have to be late!"

"You got it," agreed Al. "And before we can even get to the ticket booth, we have to cross the zoo lagoon in a pontoon boat. It could be hours before we get in!"

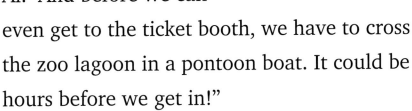

"Goody! Goody!" Bud chimed in. "Kim's ready and Mr. Long said I could have a baby baboon balloon from the zoo."

As Mr. Long lifted Bud onto the pontoon boat, Bud asked him, "Mr. Long, do you think I could be a zookeeper when I grow up?"

"That's an honorable job, Bud. As long as that tooth grows back in first!" Mr. Long replied. Bud's tooth had come out on the way to the zoo. He had folded it into a napkin and put it in his pocket. This was a wonderful day for Bud.

Once everyone had piled in, the gate closed and the pontoon left. They could see the zoo on the other side. "Nick," Bud asked, "Do you think you and Al could be brave and go in with the tiger? I would."

"If you go in with a tiger, it would not be brave," Nick said. "It would be stupid!"

The kids joked with each other until the pontoon

approached the opposite shore.

Suddenly, a gust of wind overtook the pontoon's striped roof. The boat nearly capsized, and Bud fell into the gate. Mr. Long grabbed him  just in the nick of time, but not before Bud's tooth sank to the bottom of the lagoon.

"My tooth! My tooth!" cried Bud.

"That's OK, Bud," Nick teased. "Al and I will get you a tiger's tooth!"

"Bud, you come with me. We can go and look for the baby baboon balloons. Your brother is being a creep," Kim said.

"OK. You two go while we wait in line at the ticket booth," her mom said.

Mr. Long reminded Al and Nick to behave. "Will you two go and get us a scoop of ice cream?" he asked.

When Nick and Al left for the ice cream stand, Mr. Long said, "Doris Chung. I have never seen you looking so sad. What in the name of heaven is the matter?"

"It's my class," she said. "This year I have some students who are disrespectful. They make it terrible for the other students. I wish there were something I could do."

"I'm sorry to hear that," Mr. Long replied. "One day they will realize what a good teacher you were and regret the disrespect."

The zoo map Mr. Long got from the ticket taker led them to the reptile hut. As they left, Bud said, "I can read that! It says: POLAR BEAR ➡ . Can we go, please?"

Everyone trudged off in the direction of the polar bear. "Grrrrr. I don't like these animals," Kim said. "They scare me. Let's go see the baby animals instead."

"I will be a polar bear trainer when I grow up. I thought of it a lot," said Bud.

"Yeah, Bud. Like one second." Nick and Al cackled at Bud.

Bud began to cry. "I wish I had my loose tooth back," he said. "Everybody else gets money for a tooth, but not me!"

Mrs. Chung gave Bud a hug and wiped his eyes. "I will tell your mom what happened to your tooth. It will be OK."

Soon Bud perked up. "Here it is, Kim! Look! MOOSE ➡. Come with me to see the baby moose! Mr. Long, are baby mooses meeses? When I grow up, I think I will be a moose master."

Teacher/Parent Pages

Use the following questions to stimulate language growth, imagination, conceptual relationships, and higher-level thinking skills. These activities will encourage conversation and help develop language skills. Students must know that their ideas are important and that their questions will be heard. Have fun and accept all reasonable answers while praising and encouraging questioning from the students.

Vocabulary Expansion

Describe and define these words and phrases:

win honors	pontoon boat	in the nick of time
career path	opposite shore	reptile hut
ticket booth	gust of wind	trudged off
zookeeper	bottom of the lagoon	downcast
honorable job	disrespectful students	compassion

Language Expansion Activities

1. Pretend you are a zookeeper. Identify some daily activities for a zookeeper. Make a list of your jobs and responsibilities. What is the name of your zoo?

2. Make a zoo map for the characters in the story. Go back to the text and check to make sure you have included all the animal displays mentioned in the story. Add some of your own favorites. Be sure to label the map and include a map legend in the bottom right corner.

Language Expansion Questions

1. Who were the characters in this story and where were they going?

2. Give two reasons why Bud was so excited.

3. Name the animal displays in the same order as they occurred in the story. Which was Kim's favorite? What is your favorite?

4. Bud kept saying what he wanted to be when he grew up, and it was always something different. Do you ever think of what career path you might take as an adult? Do you change your mind often, like Bud, or do you always want the same career?

5. Mrs. Chung was upset with her ninth grade class. Why? What do you think she could do about their being disrespectful?

6. Suppose that Bud had not lost his tooth in the lagoon. How would Bud's feelings and the events in the story have changed?

7. Give the "Best Animal in the Zoo" award to the animal your group likes best. What qualities does your animal possess?

8. Kim had a problem. She was always late. Do you know anybody like Kim? Why do you think some people are always late and some people are never late? What could a person do if she had the problem of being late and really wanted to be on time?

9. Everyone had to board a pontoon in order to get to the zoo gate. Have you ever been on a pontoon? What other kinds of boats can you name? What kind of boat would you like to own?

10. Judge whether or not the zoo in the story was a good one. Why do different animals need different kinds of displays?

A GOOD LOOK AT A CROOK

UNIT 29

Phonology/Orthography Concepts

- A **vowel digraph** is composed of two vowel letters (graphemes) that represent one vowel sound (phoneme).
- The vowel digraph **oo** represents two different phonemes.

Vocabulary

baboon	good	noon	smooth	*father*
balloon	goody	overtook	stood	*honest*
boost	lagoon	pontoon	stoop	*honor*
boot	look	roof	tooth	*hour*
booth	loose	scoop	zoo	*watch*
broom	moose	shampoo		

A GOOD LOOK AT
A CROOK

Story Summary:

Al and his dad are eyewitnesses to a robbery while they are at the zoo. Al sees something strange when a man sneaks around behind the ticket booth. His dad sees the man as well, and sends Al to get the zoo security guard. Al is a hero and he and his dad are given lifetime passes to the zoo. Al's story appears on the evening news.

Mrs. Chung and Mr. Long had taken Kim, Al, Nick, and Bud to the zoo. Later, they gathered for dinner at the Chungs' and remembered the good time they had had.

"I will get in touch with your mother and father, Nick, and see if they can come over in an hour or so and have dinner with us," Mrs. Chung said. "Your father is a good cook. Maybe he can help me!"

"I wonder what Mom and Dad will say," remarked Bud, "when we tell them what happened to Al!"

It had happened fast. Leaving the zoo, as the six of them had approached the ticket booth, Al had grabbed his father.

"Look, Dad! That man in the black hood is sneaking into the ticket booth! The ticket taker has probably left for the day! I got a good look at him," Al had whispered.

Kim had looked at Al with disgust. "You are always looking for a crime you can solve, Al. Honestly. You think you live in a Charlie Chan film. The only crooks in this zoo are the monkeys. They steal peanuts from other monkeys." Kim had thought Al was being silly.

But Al's dad had seen somebody, too, and they had decided to investigate. "Please take the other kids back to the car, Doris," Mr.

Long had advised. Mrs. Chung and the others had headed for the car while Mr. Long and Al stayed to get another look.

"Should we get the zoo security force, Dad?" Al was a little afraid.

"Just wait to see what he does next," Mr. Long had said. The next minute, in what seemed like a flash, Al and his dad had seen the man sneak off behind some big hedges. "We better get in touch with the security force," Al's dad had said. "He could get away if we do not act fast."

Al had raced to the security booth near the gate and had asked them to come quick.

Al had explained, "Dad and I saw this man in a black hood go into the ticket booth. We did not see anybody else in there. He had a bundle, so we were afraid that he may have taken something." The security men had raced to the hedges.

The security force followed the man's footsteps in the direction of the petting zoo. Then, just before the crook had time to escape over the railing, they grabbed him!

Al had identified the man. "I got a very good look at him," Al had said. The dishonest man  was taken to the local jail. He had stolen almost $500 from the zoo!

The director of the security force had commended Al. "That was quick thinking, son. Good thing you acted so swiftly."

The director added, "We would like to present you and your dad with lifetime passes to the zoo." Al was honored.

"Gee," said Bud with envy, "I wish I could have a free lifetime pass to the zoo."

"That's OK, Bud," said Mr. Long. "You can use my pass any hour, any day."

As the sizzling chicken breasts were lifted off the grill, Mr. Hopkins, Nick and Bud's

dad, said, "Well, it looks like we missed quite a day at the zoo. But we will not have to miss any of Doris's good food!"

Everyone liked to be invited to the Chungs' for dinner. Mrs. Chung was quite a cook. When they were seated at the table, Mrs. Hopkins asked, "Bud, Nick, you have not said anything about the animals. Which ones did you see?"

"Mom, wait a minute," interrupted Nick. "Look at the TV!"

"Direct from the zoo, our roving reporter, Brook Hingle, has an amazing story of a quick arrest this afternoon."

"This is Brook Hingle, live from the zoo. Just three hours ago, Al Long, a local seventh grade student, eyed a man sneaking from the zoo's ticket booth," he reported.

"The quick-thinking Al and his father, Albert Long, acted swiftly when they ran to the security booth to alert the men on duty."

The Channel 7 reporter went on, "Al and his father were honored with lifetime passes to the zoo. We are trying to reach Al and his father for a statement. We will return to this segment as soon as we are able to reach the Longs."

"Looks like you are going to be one popular kid at school," said Nick to Al.

"Yep," Kim added, "you two Longs really are just like Charlie Chan and his number one son!"

Teacher/Parent Pages

Use the following questions to stimulate language growth, imagination, conceptual relationships, and higher-level thinking skills. These activities will encourage conversation and help develop language skills. Students must know that their ideas are important and that their questions will be heard. Have fun and accept all reasonable answers while praising and encouraging questioning from the students.

Vocabulary Expansion

Describe and define these words and phrases:

quick-thinking	dreamer	flashback
roving reporter	local hero	dishonest
lifetime pass	ticket booth	analyze
Charlie Chan	cashier	act fast
number one son	security force	petting zoo

Language Expansion Activities

1. Dramatize this story. Let each person in your group have a turn being Al. Write a script for your dramatization and have someone videotape your production.

2. Using clay, sculpt some of the animals you would find in the petting zoo. Pick your favorite animal. Go to the media center and gather information about it. Then, write a nonfiction piece about your favorite animal from the petting zoo. Display your story so others can read it.

Language Expansion Questions

1. Explain the good deed Al and his father were able to do.

2. Make a list of all the characters in this story and describe them.

3. What did the robber wear? Why do robbers often wear black clothing? Can you think of any other time when people wear black clothing?

4. Explain why Kim thought Al was just dreaming. Was she really angry with him or maybe a little jealous?

5. Once apprehended, the robber was taken to the local jail. Imagine what happened to him when he got there. Why doesn't crime pay? What are some reasons robbers usually get caught?

6. Tell what would have happened if Bud had seen the robber first. Would anyone have believed him? Why is it harder for adults to believe younger children than older ones? Is it right?

7. This story was told through a flashback. What does that mean? Look back through the story and find the exact spot where the flashback begins. Tell how you know.

8. Doris Chung was a great cook. How does someone get a reputation for being good at something? What are you good at?

9. Al and his father received lifetime passes to the zoo. Do you think this was a good reward for them? What other kinds of rewards do you think would be appropriate for their actions?

10. Al's story made the evening TV news. How do you think he felt about that? Have you ever been on TV? What are some other ways people get their stories on TV?

A BUNDLE OF JOY

UNIT 30

Phonology/Orthography Concepts

- A **phonogram** is a **group** of letters that often represent the same sounds (phonemes).
- Diphthong syllables contain one of the two vowel glide phonemes of English: 1. */oy/, /oi/*; or 2. */ou/, /ow/*.
- The diphthongs **oi** and **oy** both represent the phoneme in b**oy**:
  - **oi** is followed by a consonant phoneme.
  - **-oy** is used at the **end** of a word or syllable.

Vocabulary

avoid	enjoy	moisture	spoiled	*aren't*
boiling	join	noise	toys	*couldn't*
boy	joy	overjoyed	trapezoid	*don't*
choice	Joy	point	Troy •	*haven't*
coins	joyful	rejoicing	turmoil	*isn't*
corduroy	loyal	Roy	voice	*shouldn't*
embroidered	moist	soiled	void	*wasn't*
				weren't
				wouldn't

A BUNDLE OF JOY

Story Summary:

Mat isn't very happy when his parents tell him that he is going to have a baby brother or sister. He runs off to talk to his friends. On the way back home, he decides that he has acted like a fool and races home to join his family's celebration.

Mat Miller felt like a lucky boy. Since he and his dad had moved to Jasper, good things had happened to them. First, his dad had opened Chick's Fish Shack.

And hadn't the kids at Mat's school seemed wonderful to him since the very first day? Then, his dad had met Pam, and last year the two had gotten married. Mat couldn't have had a better stepmother if he had chosen her himself. The truth was, Mat's life was nearly perfect.

One afternoon when Mat came home from school, he yelled, "Mom! Are you home?" Mat always yelled to see if Pam was home. When she was, she would fix him a sandwich and the two of them would enjoy a chat at the kitchen table.

"Your dad and I are in the kitchen, kiddo," Pam replied.

"Why don't you come in here and tell us what you did in school today? There's something we want to talk to you about." Pam's voice sounded cheerful.

"Mat, Pam and I are rejoicing. We have something to share with you," his dad said. "Sit here and join us."

Mat was still rejoicing over the A he had earned on his math test. He had the test paper in his backpack. "Didn't you say something, Dad? Don't we have anything to eat? What are we having for dinner? I haven't eaten since lunch."

"Son, wouldn't you like to have a little brother or sister?" asked Chick Miller.

"Why? We aren't having company for the weekend, are we? Look, Dad. Here's the

math test we got back today.
Thanks for helping me
understand the trapezoid
problems. I couldn't believe I
got an A! Even Mr. Troy said
I did great!"

"Fantastic, Mat!" Pam
wiped her hair back from her forehead. The
air was full of moisture. She was boiling
shrimp for her Lunch Hut. Her customers
enjoyed Pam's shrimp salad. "But let's sit
here for a minute. I don't think you
understood what your dad was trying to tell
you."

"What do you mean, Mom?" Mat asked.

"He was trying to tell you that you are

going to
have a little
brother or
sister. This
little bundle

of joy will be here soon. At last you will be a big brother!" Pam was excited to tell Mat that the baby was coming. Pam thought Mat would be overjoyed. But Mat just sat there silently. He didn't respond one way or the other.

Mat Miller wasn't a spoiled boy. Nobody thought so. He was a good kid who liked to help people. And he was loyal to his family. Having other children in their home was not something he had even thought of. But it seemed he didn't have a choice. This would mean a big change. He had to talk to Sam. Only Sam would understand the way he felt.

"I, uh, I am really glad for you," Mat stuttered. "I, uh, I need to get over to Sam's before four o'clock, though. We haven't finished that report for school. See you."

Pam and Chick Miller could sense that their boy wasn't rejoicing with them.

They tried to stop him, but Mat rushed to the back porch and through the yard. He hopped on his bike and raced over to Sam's.

While he was telling his story to Sam, Mat's eyes were moist. "Boy, Sam," Mat predicted, "things aren't going to be the same for me. Noise and screaming at two AM, soiled bottles, toys everywhere," Mat went on. "I bet I even have to baby-sit. I won't ever get to be with you and Nick."

"It couldn't be that bad," Sam tried to console his pal. "Your dad and mom are the greatest, Mat. I wish I could have a little brother. Just think of Nick and Bud! They tease each other," Sam continued. "But if something happened

to either one of them, wouldn't the other one be there in a flash? That's what brothers are for."

"But you forgot one thing," Mat said. "We could get a girl."

Mat began to feel bad. His mom and dad were so joyful, and he had run off to Sam's.

He hadn't even said that he would try to be a good big brother. After the hundreds of things they had done for him.

"I need to get back, Sam," he said. "I acted like a fool. I have to go back and tell Dad and Mom that I plan to be the best big brother they have ever seen!" Mat sprinted from his seat and jumped on his bike.

Teacher/Parent Pages

Use the following questions to stimulate language growth, imagination, conceptual relationships, and higher-level thinking skills. These activities will encourage conversation and help develop language skills. Students must know that their ideas are important and that their questions will be heard. Have fun and accept all reasonable answers while praising and encouraging questioning from the students.

Vocabulary Expansion

Describe and define these words and phrases:

good luck	trapezoid	bundle of joy
stepmother	moisture	elated
one way or another	customers	spoiled
disbelief	dumbfounded	loyal
weekend	shrimp salad	act like a fool

Language Expansion Activities

1. Make a list of all the events in the story in the proper sequence. What happened first? Second? Last? Compare your list with the lists of the others in your group. Decide who wrote the most complete list.

2. Take a piece of paper and divide it in half. On one side list boys' names, and on the other side list girls' names. Give yourself a set amount of time (for example, 2 minutes). How many names could you think of? The spelling doesn't have to be perfect. Again, compare your lists with the lists of the others in your group. Decide what names you might choose for your own children.

Language Expansion Questions

1. What did Mat's dad and stepmother want to talk to him about?

2. Mat did not seem to understand what his parents were trying to tell him. He was thinking about his math test and about going over to Sam's to do a report. Does this ever happen to you? What happens when you do not listen to your parents? Your teachers?

3. Discuss Mat's behavior after he realized that his parents were going to have a baby. Why did he act that way? Have you ever felt that way about anything? Compare your experience with his.

4. Mat's dad had a fish store. Mat helped his dad in the store, and Pam made fish chowder and shrimp salad. Why is it important for families who own their own businesses to help one another?

5. What kind of brother will Mat make? What kind of brother or sister would you make? How do you know?

6. The story says that Mat is not a spoiled boy. Do you know anyone who is spoiled? Why do you think he or she is spoiled?

7. How would the story have changed if Mat had been elated when he heard about the baby? Write an outline for the new story.

8. Identify ways in which Mat's parents are like your parents or another married couple that you know. In what ways are they different?

9. Predict some new activities that are in store for Mat after his brother or sister arrives.

10. Will Mat's parents have a boy or a girl? Do you know for sure? Why or why not?

FILLING A VOID

UNIT 30

Phonology/Orthography Concepts

- A **phonogram** is a **group** of letters that often represent the same sounds (phonemes).
- Diphthong syllables contain one of the two vowel glide phonemes of English: 1. /oy/, /oi/; or 2. /ou/, /ow/.
- The diphthongs **oi** and **oy** both represent the phoneme in b<u>oy</u>:
  - **oi** is followed by a consonant phoneme.
  - **-oy** is used at the **end** of a word or syllable.

Vocabulary

avoid	enjoy	moisture	spoiled	*aren't*
boiling	join	noise	toys	*couldn't*
boy	joy	overjoyed	trapezoid	*don't*
choice	Joy	point	Troy	*haven't*
coins	joyful	rejoicing	turmoil	*isn't*
corduroy	loyal	Roy	voice	*shouldn't*
embroidered	moist	soiled	void	*wasn't*
				weren't
				wouldn't

FILLING A VOID

Story Summary:

Mat's parents are expecting a baby. Mr. Miller tells Mat that the baby will fill a void in their lives, but Mat doesn't understand what his father means. Mat resents all the attention the new baby is getting, even before it is born. Then he meets Joy.

be like. What had they meant by a void? When they got up, Mat didn't feel any better.

At school, it seemed like everybody had heard about baby Joy. "Hey, Mat," Nick had yelled to him from the stairwell, "Didn't you tell them you wanted a boy? What's this girl stuff?"

Mat pretended not to hear. Inside, his feelings were so mixed up that he wasn't able to think clearly. He was waiting for the hours to pass so he could go back to Sam's and watch some TV.

"Mat, your dad will come by to pick you up at six to go to the hospital. Isn't it wonderful? Aren't you thrilled?" Sam's mom was nice, but she didn't understand.

Through the windows in the baby ward, a nurse held up a tiny pink bundle.

A band on the
finger-sized arm
said *"Joy Miller,*
girl." No baby boy
was nearly as

perfect as his sister. To his dad, Mat said, "I
won't let anybody near her when she starts
school. Can't we take her home today? She
looks just like me!"

The day Joy came home from the
hospital, Mat's pals came to see her. Sam and
Al came over first. They had a toy for Joy.
"Aren't you afraid to watch her?" Sam asked.
"I mean, like, if your mom and dad go
somewhere and you have to be here with her
by yourself."

"I don't have to," Mat
replied. "Dad and Mom said
it was my choice. But I will. I
wouldn't let someone else

take care of her. Joy is my sister."

Sam and Al didn't get the point. They had no brothers or sisters. They couldn't understand the way Mat felt.

An hour later, Nick and Bud arrived.

When the two brothers came in, Mat warned them, "Don't make too much noise. Joy is sleeping." The three of them tiptoed into her room to watch her sleep.

"Gee, Mat, I think something must have happened to her. Isn't she too little? Look at her feet. They must have shrunk." Bud hadn't ever seen a baby so tiny. "But she is probably OK, Mat. Honest."

Mat and Nick grinned at each other. Nick said, "Here, Mat. We didn't have time to get her a gift, so we got together a bunch of coins for her piggy bank."

Nick handed Mat a heavy sack, filled with coins.

The girls in Mat's class had sent a pink corduroy horse with JOY embroidered on its side. The card read: *"To Joy — a lucky little girl. Tam, Pat, Molly, and Kim."*

Mat's Uncle Roy had sent savings bonds for Joy. Everyone was sending expensive gifts. Everything that happened in the Miller home was Joy, Joy, Joy.

Mat didn't feel envy, though. It wasn't the way he had thought it would be. Instead, the turmoil and the noise and the happy voices were part of something wonderful. Joy had filled a void in their home. Joy was his sister.

Teacher/Parent Pages

Use the following questions to stimulate language growth, imagination, conceptual relationships, and higher-level thinking skills. These activities will encourage conversation and help develop language skills. Students must know that their ideas are important and that their questions will be heard. Have fun and accept all reasonable answers while praising and encouraging questioning from the students.

Vocabulary Expansion

Describe and define these words and phrases:

fill a void	envy	embroidery
chaos	keen on the prospect	instinct
savings bonds	contemplate	sibling rivalry
bundle of joy	finger-sized arm	baby shower
maternity ward	baby-sit	mixed-up feelings

Language Expansion Activities

1. Many people brought Joy gifts. If you could buy or make anything you wanted for Joy, what would it be? Draw a picture of your gift and write a description of it including its label, size, shape, color, and function.

2. As Mat gets older, Joy will probably annoy him at times. This is normal for brothers and sisters. Make a list of the ways in which brothers and sisters annoy each other. Compare your list with the others in your group. Then, discuss some good ways for brothers and sisters to get along better with each other.

Language Expansion Questions

1. Where was Mat at the beginning of the story? Why?

2. Tell what happened that should have made Mat happy. Why didn't he feel that way?

3. Mat's dad told him that Joy's arrival would fill a void in their home. Find two places in the story where Mat couldn't understand what his dad had meant. When did Mat finally understand what he had meant? Describe Mat's feelings in the end.

4. Describe how you feel when your sister or brother has a birthday party and everyone brings him or her presents. Do you think Mat was having the same kinds of feelings?

5. For months, the Millers planned for Joy's arrival. What are some of the things they did? Has your family ever redecorated?

6. Mat couldn't get to sleep while he was over at Sam's. His head was buzzing with thoughts of Joy and his new responsibilities. Do you ever have trouble sleeping because something is bothering you or something exciting is going to happen soon?

7. Would the story have changed much if Mat's parents had had a boy? Explain your answer.

8. Think of ways that Mat's life will change. Make a list of them.

9. Sam's mom thought Mat would be thrilled about the baby. No one seemed to understand how Mat really felt. Has someone ever thought they understood you when they really didn't? Describe how it makes you feel. What can you do about it?

10. Decide when the "turning point" in the story occurred.